C000243919

Supporting Phonics and Spelling

FOR AGES 9–10

Andrew Brodie

Contents

Andrew Brodie: Supporting Phonics & Spelling © A & C Black Publishers Ltd. 2006

Introduction

Supporting Phonics and Spelling is aimed at children in mainstream classrooms who have been identified as needing 'additional' or 'different' literacy support, particularly in phonics and spelling. The activities can be used by anyone working with children who fall into this category, whether you are a teacher, classroom assistant or parent.

Typically the nine to ten year-old children for whom the book is intended will be working at the levels expected of Year 3 or Year 4, or may simply need extra help in tackling the level of work appropriate for Year 5. Their difficulties may be short-term, and could be overcome with extra practice and support on a one-to-one or small group basis, or they may be long-term, where such support enables them to make progress but at a level behind their peer group. The activities in this book provide exactly what these children need – systematic repetition and practice of early phonic skills, based on a strong foundation of synthetic phonics and the best features of analytic phonics. The *Supporting Phonics and Spelling* series reflects the best practice in teaching spelling through phonics. It provides an approach that is:

- Systematic
- Multi-sensory
- Based on speaking and listening
- Linked closely to reading skills

This book is organised into three-page sets. It is vital that the teaching assistant or class teacher reads the 'Teacher's notes' on 'Sheet a' before starting the lesson. This first page in each set introduces specific phonemes and provides a good opportunity for the teacher and child to sound them out together. Children can also use their multi-sensory skills at this stage by drawing the letters in sand or making them out of dough or modelling clay. The second worksheet revises the same phonemes, but with a particular emphasis on speaking, listening and writing. The final worksheet in the set features a list of words containing the phonemes for further practice and consolidation. When used together, the three worksheets provide a thorough grounding in the phonic knowledge and skills that children need for confident reading, writing and spelling.

All the worksheets can be used on their own or alongside other literacy schemes that are already established within your school. The activities are simple and self-explanatory and the instruction text is deliberately kept to a minimum to make the pages easy to use for adults and less daunting for children to follow.

We recommend that the children use the *Supporting Phonics and Spelling* worksheets on a daily basis for approximately 20 minutes. Regular practice of previous learning is an integral part of the series. In completing the activities, teachers should place particular emphasis on speaking and listening skills. Most of the three-page sets include the opportunity to use dictation, a teaching method that may be considered old-fashioned, but when used appropriately can be both fun and rewarding. Opportunities will arise to dictate sounds, whole words and whole sentences. Initially, pupils might need help with each of these but will soon gain confidence as they experience increasing and visible success.

Children generally achieve the greatest success in an atmosphere of support and encouragement. Praise from a caring adult can be the best reward for the children's efforts. The worksheets and activities in this book will provide many opportunities for children to enjoy these successes. The development of a positive attitude and the resulting increase in self-esteem will help them with all of their schoolwork.

Definitions and explanations of terms

(Please note that some publications will give slightly different definitions.)

Phoneme

A phoneme is a unit of sound and can be represented by:
one letter e.g. /b/ as in **b**at   two letters e.g. /ee/ as in sw**ee**t
three letters e.g. /ear/ as in n**ear**
Note that a phoneme can be represented in several different ways
e.g. the sound /ee/ can be represented by:

ee as in f**ee**t	**ei** as in c**ei**ling	**ie** as in ch**ie**f
ea as in n**ea**t	**i** as in sk**i**	**e_e** as in P**e**t**e**

Vowel phoneme

A vowel phoneme makes an open sound and always contains at least one vowel – you usually have to open your mouth to say it.
Examples of vowel phonemes are:

/a/ as in b**a**t	/ie/ as in cr**ie**s	/oo/ as in b**oo**k
/ur/ as in t**ur**n	/ow/ as in t**ow**n	

Consonant phoneme

A consonant phoneme always contains at least one consonant and usually involves closing the mouth, or 'biting' the lower lip, or touching the roof of the mouth with the tongue. (There are exceptions e.g. /h/). Examples of consonant phonemes are:

/b/ as in **b**at	/f/ as in **ph**otograph
/th/ as in **th**ey	/ng/ as in si**ng**

Grapheme

A grapheme is a letter, a pair of letters or a group of letters representing a single sound e.g. **ee**, **ei**, **ie**, **ea**, **i** and **e_e** are all graphemes representing the sound /ee/.

Grapheme/phoneme correspondence

The relationship between letters and the sounds that they represent.

Digraph

A digraph consists of two letters representing a single sound. So, for example, the grapheme **ch** is a consonant digraph because it is made up of two consonants. The grapheme **ee** is a vowel digraph and although it contains a consonant, **ow** is also a vowel digraph, because it makes an open sound like a vowel does.

Split digraph

A split digraph consists of two vowels separated by a consonant to make one phoneme e.g.   **e_e** as in P**e**t**e**   **i_e** as in m**i**n**e**   **a_e** as in c**a**m**e**

Trigraph

A trigraph is a group of three letters representing a single sound.
The vowel phonemes /air/ and /ear/ are trigraphs.

Cluster

A cluster consists of two or more letters making more than one sound. For example: **t   h   r**   are three letters that can make the cluster **thr**, which consists of the phonemes /th/ and /r/.

Blending

Blending is the process of combining different sounds (phonemes) to be able to say a particular word or to make up part of a word e.g.
/sh/   /i/   /p/   can be blended to make the word ship.

/th/   /r/   are blended to make the cluster **thr**. Sometimes a cluster like this will be called a blend.

Segmenting

Segmenting is the process of splitting a word into its different phonemes to be able to spell it e.g. **ship** can be segmented into the three phonemes /sh/ /i/ /p/.

Onset and rime

The terms 'onset' and 'rime' are used together when analysing words. For example, in the word 'cat' the phoneme represented by the letter 'c' is described as the onset and the final cluster 'at' is described as the rime. Note that words that end with a particular rime always rhyme but words that rhyme do not always contain the same rime! For example, cat, rat and bat all end with the rime 'at' and all rhyme. But the words tough and muff rhyme but have the rimes 'ough' and 'uff'.

vc

vowel/consonant e.g. the word *it*

cv

consonant/vowel e.g. the word *be*

cvc

consonant/vowel/consonant e.g. the word *cat*

ccvc

consonant/consonant/vowel/consonant e.g. the word *shop*

cvcc

consonant/vowel/consonant/consonant e.g. the word *fast*

Andrew Brodie: Supporting Phonics & Spelling © A & C Black Publishers Ltd. 2006

An introduction to phonemes

Language can be analysed by considering the separate sounds that combine to make up spoken words. These sounds are called phonemes and the English language has more than forty of them. It is possible to concentrate on forty-two main phonemes but here we list forty-four phonemes including those that are commonly used only in some regions of the country.

It is helpful to look at each phoneme individually and then at some sample words that demonstrate how the phoneme is represented by different graphemes as shown in the list below. Try reading each word out loud to spot the phoneme in each one. For the simple vowel sounds the graphemes are shown in bold text.

Vowel phonemes	Sample words
/a/	b**a**t
/e/	l**e**g, gu**e**ss, h**ea**d, s**ai**d, s**ay**s
/i/	b**i**g, plant**e**d, b**u**sy, cr**y**stal, d**e**cide, **e**xact, g**ui**lt, r**e**peat
/o/	d**o**g, **ho**nest, w**a**s, qu**a**rrel, tr**ou**gh, v**au**lt, **yach**t (the ch is silent)
/u/	b**u**g, l**o**ve, bl**oo**d, c**o**mfort, r**ou**gh, y**ou**ng
/ae/	rain, day, game, navy, weigh, they, great, rein
/ee/	been, team, field, these, he, key, litre, quay, suite
/ie/	pie, high, sign, my, bite, child, guide, guy, haiku
/oe/	boat, goes, crow, cone, gold, sew
/ue/	soon, do, July, blue, chew, June, bruise, shoe, you, move, through
/oo/	book, put
/ar/	barn, bath (regional), laugh (regional), baa, half, clerk, heart, guard
/ur/	Thursday, girl, her, learn, word
/or/	born, door, warm, all, draw, cause, talk, aboard, abroad, before, four, bought, taught
/ow/	brown, found, plough
/oi/	join, toy, buoy
/air/	chair, pear, care, where, their, prayer
/ear/	near, cheer, here, weird, pier

Try saying this vowel phoneme in the sample words:

/er/	fast**er**, g**a**zump, curr**a**nt, wooll**e**n, circ**us**

Not to be confused with the phoneme /ur/, this phoneme is very similar to /u/ but is slightly different in some regions.

Consonant phonemes with sample words

/b/	bag, rub
/d/	dad, could
/f/	off, calf, fast, graph, tough
/g/	ghost, girl, bag
/h/	here, who
/j/	bridge, giraffe, huge, jet
/k/	kite, antique, cat, look, quiet, choir, sock, six (note that the sound made by the letter x is a blend of the phonemes /k/ and /s/)
/l/	leg, crawl, full
/m/	mug, climb, autumn
/n/	now, gnash, knight, sign, fun
/p/	peg, tap
/r/	run, wrote
/s/	cinema, goose, listen, psalm, scene, see, sword, yes, less
/t/	ten, sit, receipt
/v/	vest, love
/w/	wet
/wh/	when (regional)
/y/	yes
/z/	choose, was, zoo
/th/	the, with
/th/	thank, path
/ch/	cheer, such, match
/sh/	shop, rush, session, chute
/zh/	usual
/ng/	thing, think

For some phonemes you may dispute some of the examples that we have listed. This may be due to regional variations in pronunciation. Disputing the sounds is a positive step as it ensures that you are analysing them!

It is not necessary to teach the children all the graphemes for each phoneme but to be ready and aware when pupils suggest words to you to represent a particular sound. They are not wrong with their suggestions and should be praised for recognising the phoneme. You can then show them how the words that they have suggested are written but that normally the particular sound is represented by a specific grapheme.

Andrew Brodie: Supporting Phonics & Spelling © A & C Black Publishers Ltd. 2006

Examining the list of medium frequency words

These words from the medium frequency list for Years 4 and 5 do not always follow simple phonic patterns, although all of them include phonic elements that follow a typical pattern. Children will find them easier to tackle through developing the phonic skills that we are encouraging in this series of books: listening to sounds, speaking the sounds clearly and segmenting words into sounds that can be matched to appropriate letters, ie matching phonemes to appropriate graphemes.

above	birthday	first	know	paper	think	where
across	both	following	lady	place	those	while
almost	brother	found	leave	right	thought	white
along	brought	friends	light	round	through	whole
also	can't	garden	might	second	today	why
always	change	goes	money	show	together	window
animals	children	gone	morning	sister	told	without
any	clothes	great	mother	small	tries	woke
around	coming	half	much	something	turned	woken
asked	didn't	happy	near	sometimes	under	word
baby	different	head	never	sound	until	work
balloon	does	heard	number	started	upon	world
before	don't	high	often	still	used	write
began	during	I'm	only	stopped	walked	year
being	earth	important	opened	such	walking	young
below	every	inside	other	suddenly	watch	
better	eyes	jumped	outside	sure		
between	father	knew	own	swimming		

Some of these words are included in the phonic lists in this book and some are included as 'odd ones out'. You may like to introduce other words from the list as opportunities arise, supporting the children in segmenting the words to be able to spell them. Below is the list of focus words that appear in this book, though many others are included within the activities.

allow	cartoon	farm	hawk	order	slow	true
allowed	church	father	healthy	outdoors	snore	verb
already	circle	feather	her	outside	snow	voice
always	claw	few	herd	owl	sore	watch
annoy	cloud	first	horse	own	sound	weather
avoid	clown	flew	house	perfect	spoil	were
awful	clue	floor	important	person	start	whale
bark	coil	flower	indoors	phone	starts	when
before	cook	foot	jewel	photocopy	steady	which
bird	count	force	join	photograph	store	while
blew	crew	forty	knew	phrase	straw	whisper
blow	cruel	foul	know	physics	telephone	whistle
blue	cue	found	lawn	point	term	white
blur	curve	friends	leave	poor	third	whole
boil	dark	fur	look	purse	thirsty	why
book	dawn	germ	lounge	queue	those	wood
bored	different	girl	March	ready	thought	wool
born	door	glue	microphone	royal	thread	wore
bowl	doorstep	glueing	moor	shark	through	world
boy	draw	good	more	shirt	Thursday	yawn
bread	earth	graph	morning	shore	took	young
brother	enjoy	grew	mother	short	tore	
brought	enjoyable	ground	news	show	towel	
brown	enjoyed	grow	noise	shower	toy	
burn	enjoyment	happy	nurse	skirt	trapdoor	

Learning objective

| **1a** | **Phonemes** Consonants: /t/,/k/,/b/,/f/,/g/,/l/,/w/,/d/ Vowels: /oo/,/a/,/ee/ (as grapheme y) | **Target words** took, book, cook, foot, good, look, wood, wool, happy |

Worksheet 1a

- Photocopy this page and ask the child to cut out the target words.
- Discuss the words and what each word means. Help the child to read them by blending the phonemes.
- Ask him/her to identify the sounds in some of the words, the /g/, /d/ and the special sound /oo/ in the word *good*, for example.
- Discuss which word is the 'odd one out' from the list.

Worksheet 1b

- Discuss the words in the word bank at the top of the sheet before dictating the sentences below to the child. S/he may need some help in segmenting each word into its phonemes to make it easier to spell. Say each word repeatedly and slowly, encouraging the child to hear the separate sounds. The sentences for dictation are as follows:

  The cook had a look in a cookery book.
  I was not happy when the wood fell on my foot.
  Bob took some wood to make a good table.

- Encourage the child to write clearly, following the school's handwriting policy for letter formation, and to start each sentence with a capital letter and to end it with a full stop. As an extra activity ask the child to make up a sentence using the target words and to write it down.

Worksheet 1c

- This sheet includes the eight target words with the short vowel phoneme /oo/, together with the 'odd one out' word, *happy*.
- This sheet can be copied so that the left hand side can be used for display purposes and the right hand side can be used to provide the child with extra practice in writing the words. You could write each word on the first of the two writing lines so that the child can copy your writing underneath in the correct style used by your school.

TARGET WORDS

took	book	cook
foot	good	look
wood	wool	happy

Andrew Brodie: Supporting Phonics & Spelling © A & C Black Publishers Ltd. 2006

Name: _____ **Date:** _____

Read these words because you will need them in your sentences.

| cookery | table | some | make | when | fell |

Listen to your teacher. Write the sentences.

_____

_____

_____

_____

_____

_____

_____

_____

_____

_____

Write a sentence of your own using some of the target words.

_____

_____

_____

Name: _____   **Date:** _____

Words for today

took   _____

book   _____

cook   _____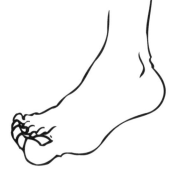

foot   _____

good   _____

look   _____

wood   _____

wool   _____

happy   _____

Andrew Brodie: Supporting Phonics & Spelling © A & C Black Publishers Ltd. 2006

Learning objective

Phonemes
Consonants: /s/,/n/,/b/,/l/,/t/,/d/,/ng/
/n/ (as grapheme kn), /sh/,/s/,/g/,/r/
Vowels: /oe/ (as grapheme ow), /i/,
/ow/ (as grapheme ou), /ie/ as split diagraph i_e)

Target words
snow, blow, bowl, know,
own, show, slow, grow,
outside

Worksheet 2a
- Photocopy this page and ask the child to cut out the target words.
- Discuss the words and what each word means. Help the child to read them by blending the phonemes.
- Ask him/her to identify the sounds in some of the words, the /b/, /l/ and /oe/ in the word *blow*, for example.
- Discuss which word is the 'odd one out' from the list.

Worksheet 2b
- Discuss the words in the word bank at the top of the sheet.
- Encourage the child to listen carefully as you say each word and then to repeat each word him/herself. Help him/her to see that there is a set of 'root words' and a set of the same words but with 'ing' added, then ask him/her to rewrite the words, sorting them into the two sets.
- Ask the child to create oral sentences which include some of the words, then to write down one of the sentences e.g. *On Monday it was snowing and the wind was blowing hard outside my window.* Encourage the child to write clearly, following the school's handwriting policy for letter formation, and to start each sentence with a capital letter and to end it with a full stop.

Worksheet 2c
- This sheet includes the eight target words with the phoneme /oe/, together with the 'odd one out' word, *outside*.
- This sheet can be copied so that the left hand side can be used for display purposes and the right hand side can be used to provide the child with extra practice in writing the words. You could write each word on the first of the two writing lines so that the child can copy your writing underneath in the correct style used by your school.

TARGET WORDS

snow	blow	bowl
know	own	show
slow	grow	outside

2b

Name: **Date:**

Read the words in the word bank.

WORD BANK

snow   blowing   bowl   know   growing   show
slowing   grow   snowing   owning   bowling
knowing   blow   showing   slow   own

⭐ Sort the words into the correct boxes.

root words	**root words + ing**

⭐ Write a sentence of your own using some of the words from the word bank.

Andrew Brodie: Supporting Phonics & Spelling © A & C Black Publishers Ltd. 2006

Name: _____   **Date:** _____

Words for today

snow   _____

blow   _____

bowl   _____

know   _____

own   _____

show   _____

slow   _____

grow   _____

outside   _____

Learning objective

Phonemes
Consonants: /f/,/l/,/b/,/ch/,/g/,/r/,/j/, /n/ (as graphemes kn and n), /k/,/t/,/d/
Vowels: /ue/ (as grapheme ew), /e/ (as grapheme ie)

Target words
flew, blew, grew, knew, few, jewel, news, crew, friends

Worksheet 3a

- Photocopy this page and ask the child to cut out the target words.

- Discuss the words and what each word means. Help the child to read them by blending the phonemes.

- Ask him/her to identify the sounds in some of the words and point out the word *knew*, which has a silent letter **k**. Encourage the child to say each word carefully. Can s/he hear a different sound made by the **ew** in some of the words? For example, the phonemes which make up the sound of **ew** in the word *few* would be /y//ue/, whereas those in the word *flew* would be /ue/.

- Discuss which word is the 'odd one out' from the list.

Worksheet 3b

- Discuss the words in the word bank at the top of the sheet. Help the child to see that there is a set of words containing the grapheme **ew** but that there are also some words with the grapheme **ow**. Point out that some of the **ew** words give the past tense of the **ow** words.

- Discuss the two complete sentences, explaining that the second sentence is about something in the past. Help the child find the correct words to fill the gaps in the following two sentences. Now ask him/her to write the appropriate words in the 'past' list, before writing the other **ew** words in the spaces provided.

- Ask the child to create oral sentences which include some of the words, then to write down one of the sentences e.g. *A few friends of the ship's crew were on the news*. Encourage the child to write clearly, following the school's handwriting policy for letter formation, and to start each sentence with a capital letter and to end it with a full stop.

Worksheet 3c

- This sheet includes the eight target words with the phoneme /ue/, together with the 'odd one out' word, *friends*.

- This sheet can be copied so that the left hand side can be used for display purposes and the right hand side can be used to provide the child with extra practice in writing the words. You could write each word on the first of the two writing lines so that the child can copy your writing underneath in the correct style used by your school.

TARGET WORDS

flew	blew	grew
knew	few	jewel
news	crew	friends

Andrew Brodie: Supporting Phonics & Spelling © A & C Black Publishers Ltd. 2006

Name: _____ **Date:** _____

Read the words in the word bank.

WORD BANK

know	blow	few	blew	news	flew	grow

crew   grew   fly   knew   friends   jewel

Read the sentences.

I know my six times table.
I knew my seven times table but I've forgotten it now.

Write the missing words in these sentences:

It's time to _____ the candles out.

Kate _____ the candles out.

Write the correct **past** words.

present	past
grow	_____
know	_____
blow	_____
fly	_____

Write the other **ew** words.

_____
_____
_____
_____

Write a sentence using some of the words above.

_____

_____

_____

Name: _____ **Date:** _____

Words for today

flew _____

blew _____

grew _____

knew _____

few _____

jewel _____

news _____

crew _____

friends _____

Andrew Brodie: Supporting Phonics & Spelling © A & C Black Publishers Ltd. 2006

4a

Learning objective

Phonemes
Consonants: /b/,/l/,/k/ (as graphemes c and q), /g/,/r/,/t/,/ng/,/m/,/p/,/n/
Vowels: /ue/,/i/,/or/,/a/

Target words
blue, clue, glue, cruel, true, cue, queue, gluing, important

Worksheet 4a

- Photocopy this page and ask the child to cut out the target words.
- Discuss the words and what each word means. Help the child to read them by blending the phonemes.
- Ask him/her to identify the sounds in some of the words, the /g/, /l/ and /ue/ in the word *glue*, for example. Note that the word *gluing* can be spelt *glueing*. The word *queue* is rather special – remind the child that a letter **q** is always followed by a letter **u**.
- Discuss which word is the 'odd one out' from the list: *important* because it does not contain the phoneme /ue/.

Worksheet 4b

- Discuss the words at the top of the sheet before dictating the following sentences to the child:

  The sea was blue and the sky was blue.
  The policewoman found an important clue.
  There was a queue of people waiting for the bus.

- S/he may need some help in segmenting each word into its phonemes to make it easier to spell. Say each word repeatedly and slowly, encouraging the child to hear the separate sounds.
- Encourage the child to write clearly, following the school's handwriting policy for letter formation, and to start each sentence with a capital letter and to end it with a full stop. As an extra activity ask the child to make up a sentence using some of the target words and to write it down.

Worksheet 4c

- This sheet includes the eight target words with the phoneme /ue/, together with the 'odd one out' word, *important*.
- This sheet can be copied so that the left hand side can be used for display purposes and the right hand side can be used to provide the child with extra practice in writing the words. You could write each word on the first of the two writing lines so that the child can copy your writing underneath in the correct style used by your school.

TARGET WORDS

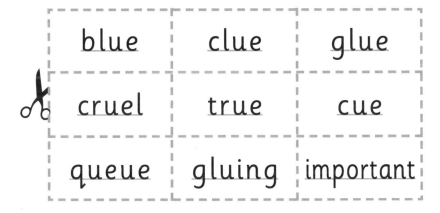

blue	clue	glue
cruel	true	cue
queue	gluing	important

Name: **Date:**

Read these words because you will need them in your sentences.

sea sky policewoman found
there people waiting

⭐ Listen to your teacher. Write the sentences.

⭐ Write a sentence of your own using some of the target words.

Andrew Brodie: Supporting Phonics & Spelling © A & C Black Publishers Ltd. 2006

Name: **Date:**

Words for today

blue   _____

clue   _____

glue   _____

cruel   _____

true   _____

cue   _____

queue   _____

gluing   _____

important   _____

Learning objective

Phonemes **Consonants:** /f/,/m/,/b/,/k/,/t/,/n/,/ch/, /s/,/d/,/sh/,/w/ **Vowels:** /ar/,/ue/ (as grapheme oo), /o/ (as grapheme a)	**Target words** farm, bark, cartoon, March, start, starts, dark, shark, watch

Worksheet 5a

- Photocopy this page and ask the child to cut out the target words.
- Discuss the words and what each word means. Help the child to read them by blending the phonemes.
- Ask him/her to identify the sounds in some of the words, the /b/, /ar/ and /k/ in the word *bark*, for example.
- Discuss which word is the 'odd one out' from the list.

Worksheet 5b

- Dictate the following words to create the word bank at the top of the sheet: **farm, bark, cartoon, March, start, starts, dark, shark, watch**.
- The child may need some help in segmenting each word into its phonemes to make it easier to spell. Say each word repeatedly and slowly, encouraging the child to hear the separate sounds.
- Ensure that the child has spelt all the words correctly, and that s/he has written the month March with a capital **M**, before asking him/her to complete the gaps in the sentences.
- Encourage the child to write clearly, following the school's handwriting policy for letter formation, and to start each sentence with a capital letter and to end it with a full stop. As an extra activity ask the child to make up a sentence using some of the target words and to write it down.

Worksheet 5c

- This sheet includes the eight target words with the phoneme /ar/, together with the 'odd one out' word, *watch*.
- This sheet can be copied so that the left hand side can be used for display purposes and the right hand side can be used to provide the child with extra practice in writing the words. You could write each word on the first of the two writing lines so that the child can copy your writing underneath in the correct style used by your school.

TARGET WORDS

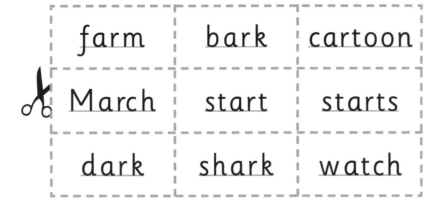

Andrew Brodie: Supporting Phonics & Spelling © A & C Black Publishers Ltd. 2006

5b **Name:** _____ **Date:** _____

Listen to your teacher. Write the words in the word bank.

WORD BANK

_____   _____   _____

_____   _____   _____

_____   _____   _____

Use the correct words to fill the gaps in these sentences:

The dog at the _____ began to _____ at the sheep.

Jasdeep watched a _____ on the television.

Sometimes it is very cold in _____ but it _____ to get warmer in April.

Write a sentence of your own using some of the target words.

_____

_____

_____

Name: **Date:**

Words for today

farm   _____

bark   _____

cartoon   _____

March   _____

start   _____

starts   _____

dark   _____

shark   _____

watch   _____

Andrew Brodie: Supporting Phonics & Spelling © A & C Black Publishers Ltd. 2006

6a

Learning objective

Phonemes
Consonants: /b/,/v/,/l/,/j/,/s/,/z/,/w/,
/k/ (as grapheme c), /d/,/n/,/p/,/t/
Vowels: /oi/,/or/ (as grapheme a),
/ae/ (as grapheme ay)

Target words
boil, coil, avoid, join, point,
spoil, noise, voice, always

Worksheet 6a

- Photocopy this page and ask the child to cut out the target words.
- Discuss the words and what each word means. Help the child to read them by blending the phonemes.
- Ask him/her to identify the sounds in some of the words. Encourage the child to say each word carefully. Can s/he hear that the letter **s** in *noise* makes a /z/ sound and that the letter **c** in *voice* makes a /s/ sound?
- Discuss which word is the 'odd one out' from the list.

Worksheet 6b

- Discuss the words in the word bank at the top of the sheet. Help the child to see that there is a set of 'root words' and a set of the same words but with 'ing' added, then ask him/her to rewrite the words, sorting them into the two sets.
- Ask him/her to create oral sentences which include some of the words or related words, then to write down one of the sentences e.g. *Children should avoid boiling water. My brother is always very noisy because he has a very loud voice.*
- Encourage the child to write clearly, following the school's handwriting policy for letter formation, and to start each sentence with a capital letter and to end it with a full stop.

Worksheet 6c

- This sheet includes the eight target words with the phoneme /oi/, together with the 'odd one out' word *always*.
- This sheet can be copied so that the left hand side can be used for display purposes and the right hand side can be used to provide the child with extra practice in writing the words. You could write each word on the first of the two writing lines so that the child can copy your writing underneath in the correct style used by your school.

TARGET WORDS

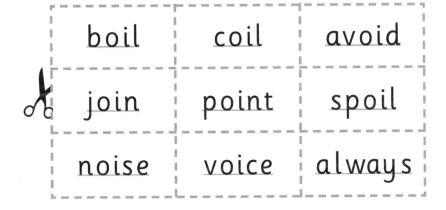

6b **Name:**   **Date:**

Read the words in the word bank.

WORD BANK

join coiling boil avoiding point pointing
spoil spoiling joining avoid boiling coil

★ Sort the words into the correct boxes.

<table>
<tr><td>

root words

_____

_____

_____

_____

_____

_____

</td><td>

root words + ing

_____

_____

_____

_____

_____

_____

</td></tr>
</table>

★ Here are some more **oi** words for you to copy.

coin   foil   noise   noisy   voice

_____ _____ _____ _____ _____

★ Write a sentence using at least one **oi** word.

_____

_____

_____

Andrew Brodie: Supporting Phonics & Spelling © A & C Black Publishers Ltd. 2006

Name: **Date:**

Words for today

boil   _____

coil   _____

avoid   _____

join   _____

point   _____

spoil   _____

noise   _____

voice   _____

always   _____

7a

Phonemes
Consonants: /b/,/r/,/n/,/l/,/j/,/m/,/t/, /y/,/ng/
Vowels: /oi/,/er/,/e/,/u/

Target words
boy, royal, annoy, enjoy, enjoyed, enjoyable, enjoyment, toy, young

Worksheet 7a

- Photocopy this page and ask the child to cut out the target words.
- Discuss the words and what each word means. Help the child to read them by blending the phonemes.
- Ask him/her to identify the sounds in some of the words e.g. the grapheme **ou** making the sound /u/, in the word *young* and the grapheme **oy** making the sound /oi/ in the word *boy*. Discuss which word is the 'odd one out' from the list: *young*, because it does not contain the phoneme /oi/.

Worksheet 7b

- Discuss the words at the top of the sheet before dictating the following sentences to the child:

  The young boy played with his new toy.
  The boy enjoyed seeing the royal family.
  Do not annoy an angry wasp.

- S/he may need some help in segmenting each word into its phonemes to make it easier to spell. Say each word repeatedly and slowly, encouraging the child to hear the separate sounds.
- Encourage the child to write clearly, following the school's handwriting policy for letter formation, and to start each sentence with a capital letter and to end it with a full stop. As an extra activity ask the child to make up a sentence using some of the target words and to write it down.

Worksheet 7c

- This sheet includes the eight target words with the vowel phoneme /oi/, together with the 'odd one out' word, *young*.
- This sheet can be copied so that the left hand side can be used for display purposes and the right hand side can be used to provide the child with extra practice in writing the words. You could write each word on the first of the two writing lines so that the child can copy your writing underneath in the correct style used by your school.

TARGET WORDS

boy	royal	enjoyed
annoy	enjoy	enjoyable
toy	young	enjoyment

Andrew Brodie: Supporting Phonics & Spelling © A & C Black Publishers Ltd. 2006

Name: **Date:**

Read these words because you will need them in your sentences.

| played   seeing   family   angry   wasp |

Listen to your teacher. Write the sentences.

_____

_____

_____

_____

_____

_____

_____

_____

Write a sentence of your own using some of the target words.

_____

_____

Name: _____   **Date:** _____

Words for today

boy   _____

royal   _____

annoy   _____

enjoy   _____

enjoyed   _____

enjoyable   _____

enjoyment   _____

toy   _____

young   _____

Andrew Brodie: Supporting Phonics & Spelling © A & C Black Publishers Ltd. 2006

8a

Learning objective

Phonemes
Consonants: /b/,/r/,/k/,/n/,/l/,/d/,/f/, /sh/,/t/,/th/
Vowels: /ow/,/er/,/ur/

Target words
brown, clown, allow, allowed, flower, owl, shower, towel, earth

Worksheet 8a

- Photocopy this page and ask the child to cut out the target words.
- Discuss the words and what each word means. Help the child to read them by blending the phonemes.
- Ask him/her to identify the sounds in some of the words, the /c/, /l/, /ow/, and /n/ in the word *clown*, for example.
- Discuss which word is the 'odd one out' from the list.

Worksheet 8b

- Discuss the words in the word bank at the top of the sheet. Help the child to see that there is a set of 'root words' and a set of the same words but with 'ing' or 'ed' added, then ask him/her to rewrite the words, sorting them into the three sets.
- S/he may need some help in segmenting each word into its phonemes to make it easier to spell. Say each word repeatedly and slowly, encouraging the child to hear the separate sounds.
- Ask the child to create oral sentences which include some of the words, then to write down one of the sentences e.g. *The owl sat on some brown earth near a red flower. "Stop clowning about in the shower," said Mum*.
- Encourage the child to write clearly, following the school's handwriting policy for letter formation, and to start each sentence with a capital letter and to end it with a full stop.

Worksheet 8c

- This sheet includes the eight target words with the phoneme /ow/, together with the 'odd one out' word, *earth*.
- This sheet can be copied so that the left hand side can be used for display purposes and the right hand side can be used to provide the child with extra practice in writing the words. You may like to write each word on the first of the two writing lines so that the child can copy your writing underneath in the correct style used by your school.

TARGET WORDS

brown	clown	allow
allowed	flower	owl
shower	towel	earth

Name: **Date:**

Read the words in the word bank.

WORD BANK

allow   browned   allowed   flowered
clowning   browning   showered   flower
allowing   flowering   shower   showering
brown   clown   clowned

Sort the words into the correct boxes.

root words	**root words + ing**	**root words + ed**

Write a sentence of your own using some of the target words.

_____

_____

_____

Andrew Brodie: Supporting Phonics & Spelling © A & C Black Publishers Ltd. 2006

Name: _____   **Date:** _____

Words for today

brown   _____

clown   _____

allow   _____

allowed   _____

flower   _____

owl   _____

shower   _____

towel   _____

earth   _____

Learning objective

Phonemes
Consonants: /s/,/n/,/d/,/k/,/l/,/t/,/f/,/g/
/r/,/h/,/j/,/th/,/z/
Vowels: /ow/,/oe/

Target words
sound, cloud, count, foul,
found, ground, house, lounge,
those

Worksheet 9a

- Photocopy this page and ask the child to cut out the target words.
- Discuss the words and what each word means. Help the child to read them by blending the phonemes.
- Ask him/her to identify the sounds in some of the words e.g. the grapheme **ou** making the sound /ow/ in the target words. Remind him/her that **ou** made the sound /u/ in the high frequency word *young* seen on an earlier sheet, and that the sound /ow/ was made with the letters **o** and **w**, on the previous set of worksheets.
- Discuss which word is the 'odd one out' from the list.

Worksheet 9b

- Look at the sheet together and explain that you will read the complete sentences and that s/he will complete each one by writing the correct word in the gap.
- Allow the child ample time to study the target words before you begin. S/he may need some help in segmenting each word into its phonemes to make it easier to spell. Say each word repeatedly and slowly, encouraging the child to hear the separate sounds.
- Now read the following sentences to the child:

  Can you count those clouds?
  Listen to the loud sound in the lounge.
  On the ground near my house there are lots of flowers growing.

- Next, ask the child to read the additional words printed in the lower part of the sheet, and to use one or more of these and/or the target words to make a sentence of their own. This could be a humorous sentence.
- The child can then be encouraged to write their sentence on the writing lines provided. Encourage the child to write in the correct style used by your school.

Worksheet 9c

- This sheet includes the eight target words with the phoneme /ow/, together with the 'odd one out' word, *those*.
- This sheet can be copied so that the left hand side can be used for display purposes and the right hand side can be used to provide the child with extra practice in writing the words. You may like to write each word on the first of the two writing lines so that the child can copy your writing in the correct style used by your school.

TARGET WORDS

sound	cloud	count
foul	found	ground
house	lounge	those

Andrew Brodie: Supporting Phonics & Spelling © A & C Black Publishers Ltd. 2006

Name: **Date:**

Listen to your teacher.
Write the missing words in the sentences.

Can you _____
those _____?

Listen to the loud _____
in the _____.

On the _____ near my
_____ there are lots
of flowers growing.

Look at these words. Use some of them in an interesting sentence.

aloud	thousand	out	trousers	mouse
blouse	trout	our	noun	

_____

_____

_____

Name: **Date:**

Words for today

sound   _____

cloud   _____

count   _____

foul   _____

found   _____

ground   _____

house   _____

lounge   _____

those   _____

Andrew Brodie: Supporting Phonics & Spelling © A & C Black Publishers Ltd. 2006

Learning objective	
Phonemes **Consonants:** /b/,/n/,/d/,/f/,/s/,/t/,/h/,/m/, /ng/,/sh/,/th/ **Vowels:** /or/,/ee/,/i/,/er/	**Target words** born, bored, force, forty, horse, morning, order, short, thought

Worksheet 10a

- Photocopy this page and ask the child to cut out the target words.
- Discuss the words and what each word means. Help the child to read them by blending the phonemes.
- Ask him/her to identify the sounds in some of the words, the /f/, /or/, /t/ and /ee/ in the word *forty*, for example. Discuss which word is the 'odd one out' from the list.
- Encourage the child to notice that whilst the sound /or/ is in all the words, *thought* is the 'odd one out' because of the **ough** spelling.

Worksheet 10b

- Dictate the following words to create the word bank at the top of the sheet: **born, bored, force, forty, horse, morning, order, short, thought**.
- S/he may need some help in segmenting each word into its phonemes to make it easier to spell. Say each word repeatedly and slowly, encouraging the child to hear the separate sounds. Ensure that the child has spelt all the words correctly before asking him/her to complete the gaps in the sentences.
- Encourage the child to write clearly, following the school's handwriting policy for letter formation, and to start each sentence with a capital letter and to end it with a full stop. As an extra activity ask the child to make up a sentence using some of the target words and to write it down.

Worksheet 10c

- This sheet includes the eight target words with the phoneme /or/, together with the 'odd one out' word, *thought*.
- This sheet can be copied so that the left hand side can be used for display purposes and the right hand side can be used to provide the child with extra practice in writing the words. You could write each word on the first of the two writing lines so that the child can copy your writing underneath in the correct style used by your school.

TARGET WORDS

born	bored	force
forty	horse	morning
order	short	thought

10b

Name: **Date:**

Listen to your teacher. Write the words in the word bank.

WORD BANK

_____   _____   _____

_____   _____   _____

_____   _____   _____

★ Use the correct words to fill the gaps in
these sentences:

I saw a _____ in a field.

This _____ I had toast
for breakfast.

_____ is one more than thirty nine.

★ Write a sentence of your own using some of the target words.

_____

_____

_____

Andrew Brodie: Supporting Phonics & Spelling © A & C Black Publishers Ltd. 2006

Name: _____ **Date:** _____

Words for today

born   _____

bored   _____

force   _____

forty   _____

horse   _____

morning   _____

order   _____

short   _____

thought   _____

Andrew Brodie: Supporting Phonics & Spelling © A & C Black Publishers Ltd. 2006

Learning objective

Phonemes
Consonants: /d/,/t/,/z/,/n/,/t/,/r/,/p/, /m/,/f/,/l/,/th/
Vowels: /or/,/ow/,/i/,/e/,/a/,/ue/

Target words
door, outdoors, indoors, doorstep, trapdoor, moor, poor, floor, through

Worksheet 11a

- Photocopy this page and ask the child to cut out the target words.
- Discuss the words and what each word means. Help the child to read them by blending the phonemes.
- Ask him/her to identify the sounds in some of the words, the /m/ and /or/ in the word *moor*, for example.
- Discuss which word is the 'odd one out' from the list.
- It would be appropriate at this point to talk about compound words. Ask the child to sort the target words into two groups – simple words and compound words.

Worksheet 11b

- Explain to the child that you will dictate each of the words and s/he will write the correct word under each of the pictures.
- Next, read the target words slowly and clearly, allowing the child plenty of time to choose which picture to write each word under. S/he may need some help in segmenting each word into its phonemes to make it easier to spell. Say each word repeatedly and slowly, encouraging the child to hear the separate sounds.
- An additional activity would be to ask the pupil to make up some sentences using the target words e.g. *The poor dog didn't know whether to stay indoors or to go outdoors. The clown went through a trapdoor in the floor.*

Worksheet 11c

- This sheet includes the eight target words with the phoneme /or/, together with the 'odd one out' word, *through*.
- This sheet can be copied so that the left hand side can be used for display purposes and the right hand side can be used to provide the child with extra practice in writing the words. You could write each word on the first of the two writing lines so that the child can copy your writing in the correct style used by your school.

TARGET WORDS

door	indoors	outdoors
moor	poor	doorstep
floor	through	trapdoor

Andrew Brodie: Supporting Phonics & Spelling © A & C Black Publishers Ltd. 2006

Name: _____   **Date:** _____

Listen to your teacher. Write the words under the correct pictures.

door   outdoors   indoors   doorstep
trapdoor   moor   poor   floor   through

_____   _____   _____

_____   _____   _____

_____   _____   _____

Name: _____ **Date:** _____

Words for today

door   _____

outdoors   _____

indoors   _____

doorstep   _____

trapdoor   _____

moor   _____

poor   _____

floor   _____

through   _____

Andrew Brodie: Supporting Phonics & Spelling © A & C Black Publishers Ltd. 2006

Learning objective

Phonemes
Consonants: /l/,/d/,/n/,/r/,/h/,/k/,/s/, /t/,/y/,/f/,/b/
Vowels: /or/,/oo/

Target words
claw, dawn, draw, hawk, lawn, straw, yawn, awful, brought

Worksheet 12a

- Photocopy this page and ask the child to cut out the target words.
- Discuss the words and what each word means. Help the child to read them by blending the phonemes.
- Ask him/her to identify the sounds in some of the words. Discuss which word is the 'odd one out' from the list and that in the word *brought* there is the same sound /or/ as in the eight target words but not made with the **aw** spelling.

Worksheet 12b

- Discuss the words at the top of the sheet before dictating the following sentences to the child:

  The hawk on the lawn has sharp claws.
  At dawn I saw an awful monster.
  "I brought some straw to sleep on," said the boy as he yawned loudly.

- S/he may need some help in segmenting each word into its phonemes to make it easier to spell.
- Say each word repeatedly and slowly, encouraging the child to hear the separate sounds.
- Encourage the child to write clearly, following the school's handwriting policy for letter formation, and to start each sentence with a capital letter and to end it with a full stop.
- Talk to the pupil about using speech marks and about adding **ed** to put *yawn* into the past tense. As an extra activity ask the child to make up a sentence using some of the target words and to write it down.

Worksheet 12c

- This sheet includes the eight target words with the vowel phoneme /or/, together with the 'odd one out' word *brought*.
- This sheet can be copied so that the left hand side can be used for display purposes and the right hand side can be used to provide the child with extra practice in writing the words. You could write each word on the first of the two writing lines so that the child can copy your writing underneath in the correct style used by your school.

TARGET WORDS

claw	dawn	draw
hawk	lawn	straw
yawn	awful	brought

Name: **Date:**

Read these words because you will need them in your sentences.

sharp	monster	sleep	loudly

★ Listen to your teacher. Write the sentences.

★ Write a sentence of your own using some of the target words.

Andrew Brodie: Supporting Phonics & Spelling © A & C Black Publishers Ltd. 2006

Name: **Date:**

Words for today

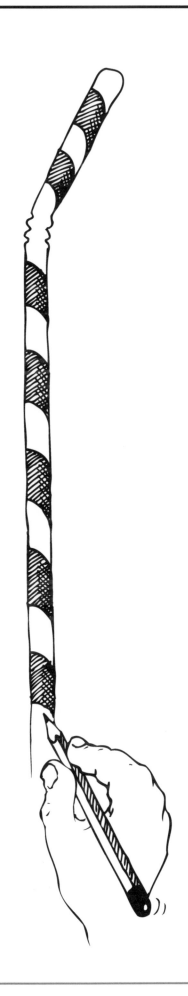

claw   _____

dawn   _____

draw   _____

hawk   _____

lawn   _____

straw   _____

yawn   _____

awful   _____

brought   _____

Learning objective

13a **Phonemes** **Consonants:** /m/,/b/,/f/,/sh/,/s/,/n/,/t/, /w/,/th/ **Vowels:** /ee/,/or/,/u/,/er/	**Target words** more, before, shore, snore, sore, store, tore, wore, mother

Worksheet 13a

- Photocopy this page and ask the child to cut out the target words.
- Discuss the words and what each word means. Help the child to read them by blending the phonemes.
- Ask him/her to identify the sounds in some of the words e.g. the grapheme **ore** making the sound /or/ in the target words.
- Discuss which word is the 'odd one out' from the list.

Worksheet 13b

- Look at this sheet together and explain that you will read the complete sentences and that s/he will complete each one by writing the correct word in the gap.
- Allow the child ample time to study the target words before you begin. S/he may need some help in segmenting each word into its phonemes to make it easier to spell. Say each word repeatedly and slowly, encouraging the child to hear the separate sounds.
- Now read the following sentences:

  My mother and father wore blue shoes.
  A stone hit my forehead and made it very sore.
  I would like to do more work before I go home.

- Next, ask the child to read the additional words printed in the lower part of the sheet, and to use one or more of these and/or the target words to make a sentence of their own. This could be a humorous sentence.
- The child can then be encouraged to write their sentence on the writing lines provided. Encourage the child to write in the correct style used by your school.

Sheet 13c

- This sheet includes the eight target words with the phoneme /or/, together with the 'odd one out' word, *mother*.
- This sheet can be copied so that the left hand side can be used for display purposes and the right hand side can be used to provide the child with extra practice in writing the words. You could write each word on the first of the two writing lines so that the child can copy your writing underneath in the correct style used by your school.

TARGET WORDS

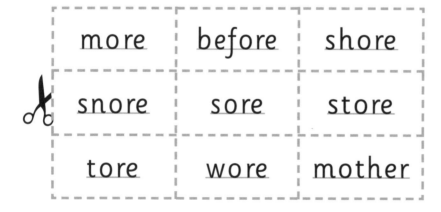

Andrew Brodie: Supporting Phonics & Spelling © A & C Black Publishers Ltd. 2006

Name: _____   **Date:** _____

Look at the sentences below. Listen to your teacher.

Write the missing words in the sentences.

My _____ and father _____

blue shoes.

A stone hit my forehead

and made it very _____.

I would like to do _____ work

_____ I go home.

Look at these words. Use some of them in an interesting sentence.

chore	core	bore	shore
snore	store	tore	

_____

_____

_____

Name: _____   **Date:** _____

Words for today

more   _____

before   _____

shore   _____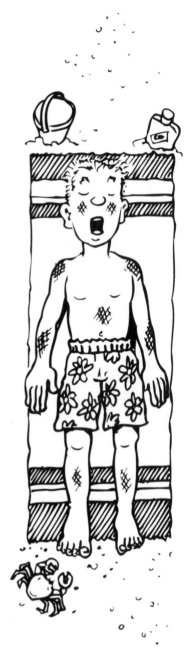

snore   _____

sore   _____

store   _____

tore   _____

wore   _____

mother   _____

Andrew Brodie: Supporting Phonics & Spelling © A & C Black Publishers Ltd. 2006

Phonemes	**Target words**
Consonants: /b/,/d/,/s/,/k/,/l/,/f/,/t/,/g/, /sh/,/th/,/r/ **Vowels:** /ur/,/ee/,/u/,/er/	bird, circle, first, girl, shirt, skirt, third, thirsty, brother

Worksheet 14a

- Photocopy this page and ask the child to cut out the target words.
- Discuss the words and help the child to read them by blending the phonemes. Support the child in deciding what each word means. Ask him/her to identify the sounds in some of the words.
- Discuss which word is the 'odd one out' from the list.

Worksheet 14b

- Look at this sheet together and explain that you will provide any help needed to read the clues, and that s/he will complete each clue by writing the correct word on the line provided.
- Allow the child ample time to study the target words before you begin. S/he may need some help in segmenting each word into its phonemes to make it easier to spell. Say each word repeatedly and slowly, encouraging the child to hear the separate sounds.
- An additional activity would be to ask the child to make up some sentences incorporating some of the target words. You could ask the child to write one of their sentences encouraging him/her to write in the correct style used by your school. If the child finds difficulty in creating his/her own sentences you could help with some examples:

  The girl wore a shirt and a skirt.
  The bird flew round in a circle.

Worksheet 14c

- This sheet includes the eight target words with the phoneme /ur/, together with the 'odd one out' word, *brother*.
- This sheet can be copied so that the left hand side can be used for display purposes and the right hand side can be used to provide the child with extra practice in writing the words. You may like to write each word on the first of the two writing lines so that the child can copy your writing underneath in the correct style used by your school.

TARGET WORDS

bird	circle	first
girl	shirt	skirt
third	thirsty	brother

★ Read the clues. Write the correct words on the lines.

A round shape   _____

The winner is this   _____

A young female   _____

Needing a drink   _____

After second   _____

A sparrow is one of these   _____

My mother's son is this to me   _____

Two items of clothing   1. _____

                           2. _____

★ Now write your own sentence using some of the target words.

_____

_____

_____

Name: _____   **Date:** _____

Words for today

bird   _____

circle   _____

first   _____

girl   _____

shirt   _____

skirt   _____

third   _____

thirsty   _____

brother   _____

15a

Learning objective

Phonemes
Consonants: /f/,/p/,/l/,/b/,/th/,/z/,/d/,/n/, /ch/,/k/,/v/,/s/,/w/
Vowels: /ur/,/ae/

Target words
fur, nurse, blur, Thursday, burn, church, curve, purse, world

Worksheet 15a

- Photocopy this page and ask the child to cut out the target words.
- Discuss the words and what each word means. Help the child to read them by blending the phonemes.
- Ask him/her to identify the sounds in some of the words and point out the capital **T** needed in the word *Thursday*.
- Discuss which word is the 'odd one out' from the list. It is important to ensure the child realises that it has the same /ur/ sound but with the spelling **or**.

Worksheet 15b

- Look at the sheet together and explain that you will dictate each of the words and s/he will write the word in the correct place on or around the picture.
- Next read the target words slowly and clearly allowing the pupil plenty of time to choose where to write each word.
- S/he may need some help in segmenting each word into its phonemes to make it easier to spell. Say each word repeatedly and slowly, encouraging the child to hear the separate sounds.
- An additional activity would be to ask the pupil to make up some sentences using the target words e.g.

  On Thursday the nurse went to church.
  The cat has very soft fur.

Worksheet 15c

- This sheet includes the eight target words with the phoneme /ur/, together with the 'odd one out' word, *world*.
- This sheet can be copied so that the left hand side can be used for display purposes and the right hand side can be used to provide the child with extra practice in writing the words. You may like to write each word on the first of the two writing lines so that the child can copy your writing underneath in the correct style used by your school.

TARGET WORDS

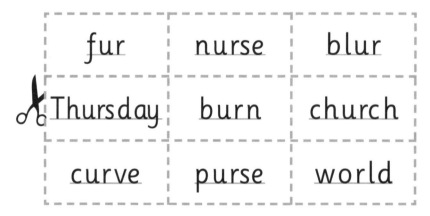

fur	nurse	blur
Thursday	burn	church
curve	purse	world

Andrew Brodie: Supporting Phonics & Spelling © A & C Black Publishers Ltd. 2006

15b

Name: _____   **Date:** _____

Listen to your teacher. Write the words in the correct places.

THIS SHOP IS CLOSED ON

NEWS
FIRE AT COUNTRY HOUSE

Name: **Date:**

Words for today

fur   _____

nurse   _____

blur   _____

Thursday   _____

burn   _____

church   _____

curve   _____

purse   _____

world   _____

Andrew Brodie: Supporting Phonics & Spelling © A & C Black Publishers Ltd. 2006

Learning objective

Phonemes	Target words
Consonants: /wh/ or /w/ (regional), /n/,/t/,/l/,/s/,/p/,/ch/,/h/ **Vowels:** /e/,/ie/,/ae/,/i/,/er/,/oe/	when, why, white, while, whale, whisper, whistle, which, whole

Worksheet 16a

- Photocopy this page and ask the child to cut out the target words.
- Discuss the words and what each word means. Help the child to read them by blending the phonemes.
- Ask him/her to identify the sounds in some of the words. Discuss which word is the 'odd one out' from the list.
- Point out that although the word *whole* has the same **wh** spelling as the others it has the phoneme /h/ making it the 'odd one out'.
- Also talk about which of the words are often used in questions, and thus where question marks are to be found in sentences.

Worksheet 16b

- Look at the sheet together and explain that you will read the complete sentences and that the child will complete each one by writing the correct word in the gap.
- Allow the pupil ample time to study the target words before you begin. S/he may need some help in segmenting each word into its phonemes to make it easier to spell. Say each word repeatedly and slowly, encouraging the child to hear the separate sounds.
- Read the following sentences:

Why do white whales swim quickly?
I whistle when I feel happy.
The whole class can whisper quietly.

- Next ask the child to read the additional words printed in the lower part of the sheet, and to use one or more of these and/or the target words to make a sentence of their own. This could be a humorous sentence. The child can then be encouraged to write their sentence on the writing lines provided using the correct style used by your school.

Worksheet 16c

- This sheet includes the eight target words with the phoneme /wh/, together with the 'odd one out' word, *whole*.
- This sheet can be copied so that the left hand side can be used for display purposes and the right hand side can be used to provide the child with extra practice in writing the words. You could write each word on the first of the two writing lines so that the child can copy your writing underneath in the correct style used by your school.

TARGET WORDS

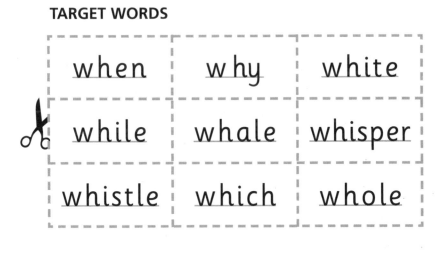

when	why	white
while	whale	whisper
whistle	which	whole

Andrew Brodie: Supporting Phonics & Spelling © A & C Black Publishers Ltd. 2006

16b **Name:**   **Date:**

Look at the sentences below. Listen to your teacher.

⭐ Write the missing words in the sentences.

_____ do _____
_____ swim quickly?

I _____ _____
I feel happy.

The _____ class can
_____ quietly.

⭐ Look at these words. Use some of them in an interesting sentence.
Write your sentence.

what	whether	whisker	whip	wheat	wheel

_____

_____

_____

Andrew Brodie: Supporting Phonics & Spelling © A & C Black Publishers Ltd. 2006

Name: _____   **Date:** _____

Words for today

when   _____

why   _____

white   _____

while   _____

whale   _____

whisper   _____

whistle   _____

which   _____

whole   _____

17a

Learning objective

Phonemes
Consonants: /h/,/d/,/p/,/f/,/k/,/t/,/s/,/n/, /m/,/v/,/b/,/w/,/j/,/th/
Vowels: /ur/,/e/,/u/,/ar/,/er/

Target words
her, herd, perfect, person, term, verb, were, germ, father

Worksheet 17a

- Photocopy this page and ask the child to cut out the target words.

- Discuss the words and what each word means. Help the child to read them by blending the phonemes.

- Ask him/her to identify the sounds in some of the words. Discuss which word is the 'odd one out' from the list. Can the child identify the fact that although *father* ends with the grapheme **er** it is not making the phoneme /ur/ as it is in the word *herd*? Please note that there may be some regional variations.

Worksheet 17b

- Discuss the words at the top of the sheet before dictating the following sentences to the child:

  Last term we were learning about nouns, adjectives and verbs.
  My father saw a herd of perfect brown cows.
  She washed her hands to remove any harmful germs.

- S/he may need some help in segmenting each word into its phonemes to make it easier to spell. Say each word repeatedly and slowly, encouraging the child to hear the separate sounds.

- Encourage the child to write clearly, following the school's handwriting policy for letter formation, and to start each sentence with a capital letter and to end it with a full stop.

- As an extra activity ask the child to make up a sentence and to write it down. Encourage the use of the word *person* in that sentence.

Worksheet 17c

- This sheet includes the eight target words with the vowel phoneme /ur/, together with the 'odd one out' word, *father*.

- This sheet can be copied so that the left hand side can be used for display purposes and the right hand side can be used to provide the child with extra practice in writing the words. You could write each word on the first of the two writing lines so that the child can copy your writing in the correct style used by your school.

TARGET WORDS

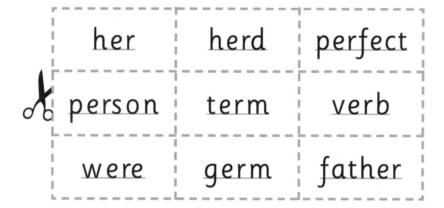

her	herd	perfect
person	term	verb
were	germ	father

Andrew Brodie: Supporting Phonics & Spelling © A & C Black Publishers Ltd. 2006

Name: **Date:**

Read these words because you will need them in your sentences.

last	learning	nouns	adjectives
cows	washed	remove	harmful

Listen to your teacher. Write the sentences.

Write a sentence of your own using some of the target words.

Name: **Date:**

Words for today

her   _____

herd   _____

perfect   _____

person   _____

term   _____

verb   _____

were   _____

germ   _____

father   _____

Andrew Brodie: Supporting Phonics & Spelling © A & C Black Publishers Ltd. 2006

18a

Phonemes **Consonants:** /f/,/g/,/r/,/t/,/l/,/n/,/m/,/k/, /p/,/z/,/s/,/d/ **Vowels:** /oe/,/a/ or /ar/ (regional), /e/,/er/, /ie/,/ar/,/o/,/ee/,/ae/,/i/	**Target words** phone, graph, telephone, microphone, photograph, photocopy, phrase, physics, different

Worksheet 18a

- Photocopy this page and ask the child to cut out the target words.
- Discuss the words and what each word means. Help the child to read them by blending the phonemes.
- Discuss which word is the 'odd one out' from the list. It would be appropriate at this point to talk about the meaning of the words and the reasons for the similarity between some of them e.g. *photocopy* and *photograph* (photo meaning light). These are not easy words but they are all words that will be familiar to the pupil as they are in everyday use.

Worksheet 18b

- Look at this sheet together. Explain to the child that you will dictate some of the words and that s/he will write the correct word under each of the pictures.
- Next read the words slowly and clearly allowing the pupil plenty of time to choose where to write each word (**graph, telephone, microphone, photograph, photocopy**).
- S/he may need some help in segmenting each word into its phonemes to make it easier to spell. Say each word repeatedly and slowly, encouraging the child to hear the separate sounds.
- An additional activity would be to ask the child to sort the target words into the boxes at the bottom of the page according to the number of syllables in each word.

Worksheet 18c

- This sheet includes the eight target words with the phoneme /f/, together with the 'odd one out' word, *different*.
- This sheet can be copied so that the left hand side can be used for display purposes and the right hand side can be used to provide the child with extra practice in writing the words. You may like to write each word on the first of the two writing lines so that the child can copy your writing in the correct style used by your school.

TARGET WORDS

phone	graph	telephone
microphone	photograph	photocopy
phrase	physics	different

Name: **Date:**

Listen to your teacher. Write the words under the correct pictures.

graph
telephone
microphone
photograph
photocopy

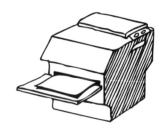

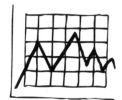

⭐ Now sort the words into the correct boxes below.

1 syllable

----

2 syllables

----

3 syllables

----

4 syllables

Andrew Brodie: Supporting Phonics & Spelling © A & C Black Publishers Ltd. 2006

Name: _____   **Date:** _____

Words for today

phone   _____

graph   _____

telephone   _____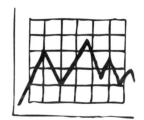

microphone   _____

photograph   _____

photocopy   _____

phrase   _____

physics   _____

different   _____

Learning objective

| **Phonemes**
 Consonants: /f/,/th/,/w/,/b/,/r/,/d/,/l/, /s/,/t/,/h/,/v/
 Vowels: /e/,/er/,/ee/ | **Target words**
 feather, weather, bread, thread, ready, already, steady, healthy, leave |

19a

Worksheet 19a

- Photocopy this page and ask the child to cut out the target words.
- Discuss the words and what each word means. Help the child to read them by blending the phonemes.
- Ask him/her to identify the sounds in some of the words. Discuss which word is the 'odd one out' from the list. Point out that the word *leave* is the odd one out because of its /ee/ sound even though the **ea** spelling is the same as in the target words.

Worksheet 19b

- Discuss the words at the top of the sheet before dictating the following sentences to the child:

  In good weather I leave the windows open.
  When you are ready please hold the thread steady.
  Feed bread to healthy ducks with long feathers.

- S/he may need some help in segmenting each word into its phonemes to make it easier to spell. Say each word repeatedly and slowly, encouraging the child to hear the separate sounds.
- Encourage the child to write clearly, following the school's handwriting policy for letter formation, and to start each sentence with a capital letter and to end it with a full stop. As an extra activity ask the child to make up a sentence using some of the target words and to write it down.

Worksheet 19c

- This sheet includes the eight target words with the vowel phoneme /e/, together with the 'odd one out' word, *leave*.
- This sheet can be copied so that the left hand side can be used for display purposes and the right hand side can be used to provide the child with extra practice in writing the words. You may like to write each word on the first of the two writing lines so that the child can copy your writing underneath in the correct style used by your school.

TARGET WORDS

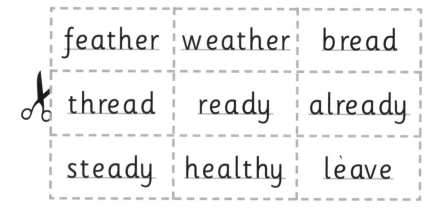

feather	weather	bread
thread	ready	already
steady	healthy	leave

Andrew Brodie: Supporting Phonics & Spelling © A & C Black Publishers Ltd. 2006

Name: _____ **Date:** _____

Read these words because you will need them in your sentences.

| good | windows | please | feed | ducks | long |

Listen to your teacher. Write the sentences.

_____

_____

_____

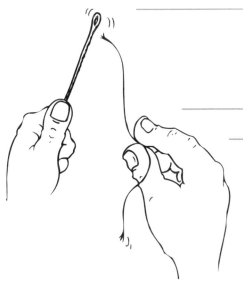

_____

_____

_____

_____

_____

_____

Write a sentence of your own using some of the target words.

_____

_____

19c

Name: _____ **Date:** _____

Words for today

feather   _____

weather   _____

bread   _____

thread   _____

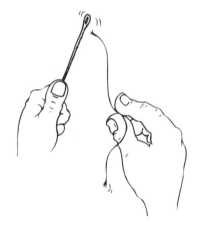

ready   _____

already   _____

steady   _____

healthy   _____

leave   _____

Andrew Brodie: Supporting Phonics & Spelling © A & C Black Publishers Ltd. 2006